MW00817467

More praise for *Write to Heal*

"Beautiful work. As a therapist, I would recommend this to many of my clients looking to find creative ways of healing. As a person, this book is encouraging and thought-provoking. The book encourages us to step out of our comfort zone and examine ourselves in a safe, creative and encouraging way. It's so important for books to be understood by all readers— not just us with the expertise of jargon in the helping professions. This book gently, but purposefully and intentionally, guides us to areas of growth we may not have been otherwise conscious of. It's a must-have for lovers of creative writing, self-love and healing."

-Darla Wheatman
Trauma Therapist

"There are few people in the world that can connect with others through their words. Rachel is that person! I can, unequivocally, say that this workbook will be life-changing for millions of people who are willing to give it a chance. I've truly been enlightened, and I am excited to start applying what I'm learning about myself."

-Jenna Edwards, MA, NCC

"This workbook has forced me to look at parts of myself I didn't even know were there. Through these prompts, I have uncovered hidden desires and have found my creative voice. Write to Heal has given me the wisdom that my words matter and that they are worth sharing with the world."

-Shelby Lavery
Freelance Social Media Manager and Storyteller

also by Rachel Havekost

Where the River Flows: A Memoir

The Inner Child Journal

The Self-Healer's Journal

The Grief Workbook

WRITE to HEAL

Turn your Wounds into Wisdom.

WRITE
to HEAL

30 Questions to Meet Yourself, Unlock Creative Wisdom, & Find the Courage to Tell Your Story.

by rachel havekost

Copyright © 2022 Rachel Havekost
All rights reserved.
ISBN 978-1-7360992-4-7

For my mother & father, who could have left when I wrote my story
but instead, asked the question,
"how can I be a part of the one you're telling?"

What if instead of trying to change
that which you do not love,
you learned to love
that which you cannot change.

table of contents

HOW TO USE THIS BOOK

WRITE *to* HEAL

---

think of this book as a loving guide.

use these prompts like gentle inquiries from a lover or friend
opportunities to open softly
as peonies & tulips
beside someone who wants to see you bloom
and grow

notice the evolution of your writing
as it changes with the opening of your body
for when we ask the hard questions
& answer truthfully
we attend to the parts of ourselves we've hidden away
and those dark pits that squirm and wriggle inside us
crack open
dissolve
and become light.

this book can be whatever you need it to be:

a map home to yourself
permission to use your voice after years of silence
healing for you, and you alone
or healing for us, the ones admiring the gardens you grow.

and if you're open,
you'll find that maybe
the healing you feel could be felt by us all.

what is writing to heal?

What started as a free writing challenge quickly transformed into a system for cracking wide open in order to witness fully who I was, and what stories were buried inside me and waiting to be told.

In the summer of 2021, I had just published my memoir *Where the River Flows.* After spending a year re-living my eating disorder and divorce, I fell into a depression that almost ended my life.

Writing is one of the main vehicles for finding myself again when I'm in the darkness. It's how I alchemize the pain, make sense of the nonsensical, and transmute the trudging-through-the-trenches into wisdom that hopefully helps someone who comes after me.

To hold myself accountable, and perhaps help someone else along the way, I made a free writing challenge called "Write to Heal," which contained 30 days of prompts that followed the path through those trenches:

→ Get clear on why I show up to the trenches in the first place
→ Honor any injuries or scrapes that need healing before taking the journey
→ Cultivate the necessary tools and collect the required equipment to make the trek
→ Embark on the journey forward

WRITE *to* HEAL

This is the path Write to Heal takes you on.

A 30-day process of sowing seeds, leaving what's heavy behind, and proceeding onward with courage and wisdom to show others the way.

This workbook is an extension of that writing challenge, with updated prompts, a clearer structure, and more defined goals and growing points along the way.

My hope is that you find healing, purpose, and growth—and perhaps the wisdom and courage to share what you learn in the end.

how to use this book

This book is constructed as a guided journal or workbook.

For thirty days, you'll have prompts that guide you on a journey of self-discovery, inner child healing, shadow work, grief and loss, growth and becoming, identity and self.

The prompts are divided into four sections. You'll have a chance to reflect at the end of each week.

Each week has a theme, which builds upon the previous week. The idea is to support you in *healing the past, finding security and safety in the present,* and *clarifying your purpose* so that you may find your voice and the courage to share your story.

Week One: *Seeds*

The first week of prompts will invite you to meet yourself where you're at *today*, at the start of this process. You'll get clear on your current life situation, self-perception, and your intentions with this process.

So often, we think we have to arrive at some all-knowing state or be "fully healed" before we can offer our wisdom or story. This couldn't be further from the truth.

If we are always waiting until we've arrived in order to start, we will never start—*that's the paradox of perfectionism.*

Instead, we have to meet ourselves where we are. We have to acknowledge and accept that this is our starting point—wherever that is—and move forward from that place instead of waiting for an invisible benchmark to grant us permission to rise.

Rise now, from wherever you're sitting, and take steps in the direction you want to go. Week one will allow you to clarify where you're starting from and name the direction. You'll pinpoint a destination, recognize the distance from here to there, and give yourself permission to start.

Week Two: *Shedding*

Week two will take you through a healing and letting go process. In order to write about our past, we have to go there. This can bring up a lot of pain. When I wrote my memoir, I had to go back in time and re-live my childhood. I had to unpack my relationships with my parents, I had to write the story of the death of my high school sweetheart, and I had to fall in love with my husband all over again while simultaneously grieving our divorce. It was horribly traumatic, and now that I've done this work, I wish I'd had more support in the rewinding process.

These prompts will hopefully illicit stories that may be worth sharing, while also helping you heal, accept, or resolve pain that still lingers. My hope is that this part of the process will provide you with relief and awareness of the past, so that when you begin the writing process you have effectively shed (or begun to shed) that which feels heavy.

Week two will likely be the most painful. Remember you do not have to do this every single day—you can break this 30-day workbook up and let it take as long as you need it to. In fact, I encourage you to rest. I encourage you to go slow. There is no rush. Trees don't grow overnight—take your time.

Week Three: *Planting*

This week you will start to take that seed—your *why*, and plant it. You will find that this week's prompts will help you start to think about what kind of soil, environment, and watering your seed needs to grow, and to grow well. You'll get clear on who your story may help, how you might want to tell your story, and what your values or boundaries are as a writer, leader, or creator.

You'll also notice many of the prompts are designed to provide you with skills to *manage* leadership. You'll start to cultivate softness, self-compassion, and skills to avoid self-sabotage. You will build a foundation of self to keep you solid and sturdy as you blossom and grow.

Week Four: *Garden*

The final week is all about expanding beyond your singular self and growing into communities. Finding ways to share your story with others from a place of rooted confidence, purpose, and passion.

You'll experiment with chapter writing, book writing, and storytelling. You'll assess whether your seed reflects your mission and consider ways you might enter into the world as a healing writer, leader, or creator.

At times, I have included short stories of my own healing. Small invitations to connect with me so you feel less alone on this path.

Sharing your story is brave. Period. The process of writing about our lives—especially the hardship and darkness, is painful. And, it can be incredibly healing.

My hope is that these prompts offer both. A chance to heal, and a chance to share.

Let's begin.

–Rachel

tips & suggestions

Organization

Keep all of your writing for the whole challenge in the same place. Whether you choose a notebook, computer, or phone, I suggest keeping all the prompts and answers in the same spot. This way you can easily go back and review all the incredible work you did in one place.

If you are intending on using what comes from these prompts for any potential published work, I suggest you do *all* of your writing on a Word Document.

This is because a) converting handwritten work to typed documents is a nightmare, and b) manuscripts are most easily formatted in Microsoft Word.

If you don't have Microsoft Word, I suggest Google Docs, which are easiest to convert down the road.

Environment

Find a safe, comfortable cozy space to write. Treat this like you would your morning routine—the more at peace, calm, and focused you are, the more you'll get out of the exercise

Mindset

Be kind to yourself. Primarily, these prompts are for *you*. There is no right or wrong way to do this. I have had days where I sit down with a writing prompt and nothing comes out. Literally, zero words. That is ok! That is *part* of the process. Sometimes all we do is stare at a laptop in silence and feel frustrated, and that is still a part of the creative work.

One Day at a Time

My invitation is to do one prompt/day. Some of the prompts may elicit heavy emotions—its important you rest, decompress, and take care of your heart along the way. There are also specific tips for certain days, so lookout for those.

Support

Tell your friends, family, therapist, or coach that you're embarking on this journey! Do it with a friend! The more support we have when trying to accomplish a goal or heal our hearts, the more likely we are to succeed.

I have a private writing group open to anyone who has taken my Wounds to Wisdom writing masterclass, so if you're interested in learning more about book publishing & seeking support you can check it out on my website: www.rachelhavekost.com

Finally, I am always here to connect on Instagram @rachel_havekost. I would love to see what is born from your writing. Feel free to tag me or use the hashtag #writetohealwithrach

WRITE *to* HEAL

week one

---

seeds.

I used to think my life needed purpose.

Now I know
my purpose
needs life.

WRITE *to* HEAL

day one:
intentions

Today is all about your *why*.

Think of your *why* as a seed. It is the beginning of the life of a tree, it is what you plant in the soil and choose to grow. It informs the direction that tree grows, the kinds of leaves it bears, the birds it attracts, and the environment it needs to flourish. Whether your seed here is planted for the duration of this workbook or for the life of your writing is not important. What's important is that you get clear on your *why*, so that you can plant this seed with intention, purpose, and direction.

Today's Prompt: Write a letter of intention *to yourself.*

Think of this as a letter to your future self—a promise you are making to yourself, or a commitment to yourself for engaging in this workbook.

Here are some questions you can think about to get started with the writing:

→ Why are you using this workbook?

→ What are you hoping to accomplish?

→ In what ways are you stuck, blocked, or lost, and how do you hope to change as a result of this process?

→ What would it mean for you to commit to this month of writing?

→ What kind of attitude, outlook, or approach will you take with the writing?

WEEK ONE

date: _____

you may use the space below to write or choose to write on your computer.

WRITE *to* HEAL

day two:
how far you've come

Perfectionism begs us to never mess up again. Courage reminds us that our mess is part of the growth cycle.

So often, we beat ourselves up in the present day—we kick ourselves for not following through on a commitment or not keeping a promise to ourselves. We may have a setback and feel like we're starting over, or find ourselves facing patterns or habits we just can't seem to unlearn.

We often forget to see how even in the mess, the mistakes, the failures and flaws, *we are still different and changed from our past selves.* Today's prompt is all about celebrating our successes (which we rarely allow ourselves to do).

Today's Prompt: *Acknowledge how far you've come.*

Think about yourself in the recent past. It can be two weeks ago, four weeks ago, or six weeks ago. Make a list of the ways in which you've grown, changed, adapted, learned, softened, or whatever it might be since then.

You can answer this in list format or as a narrative.

Tips + Suggestions:

→ **Challenges in this exercise might include** our tendency to be self-critical or only look for the ways in which we *haven't* grown or changed. We may also look back and remember goals we set or ways we wanted to change/grow but didn't. I invite you to try and focus on ways you have grown or changed, maybe in *spite* of the fact that you didn't accomplish what you thought you might.

→ **Find small wins.** This doesn't have to reflect anything enormous, it can be as simple as "since May, I have found myself smiling more when I look in the mirror" or "I have a little less anxiety in social situations than I used to."

→ **The goal of this exercise** is to train your brain to start looking for the positive aspects of our past to present narratives, rather than the negative. We tend to look back and only find/look for the bad, and this exercise is stretching the muscle that looks for the good.

WEEK ONE

date: _____

you may use the space below to write or choose to write on your computer.

WRITE *to* HEAL

day three:
dream life

Today, you get to dream. To imagine. To let go of what is not and lean into *what could be.*

I want you to consider the possibility that the greater you dream, the greater your reality. No, I'm not suggesting that simply by thinking about a lover or material items or a wanted destination they will fall into your lap. And, by visualizing, very clearly, what we desire, we bring into our awareness a potential future or goal, and our minds subconsciously start to answer the question, "how could I make this happen?"

Today's Prompt: Write your *dream life.*

Imagine what you *want* your life to be like in 10 years from now. Write a detailed, sensory, fantastical description of that life.

For this prompt, *don't worry about the how.* Don't worry about how you'll get the life you want or what you'll have to do between now and then to make it happen. Let yourself have and be everything you desire.

Don't hold back. Fantasize. Include everything you've ever wanted. *For* yourself and *about* yourself. Imagine the most incredible future for yourself and write it out.

Here are some questions you can think about to get started with the writing:

→ What kind of a person am I?

→ Who is there, and what are my relationships like?

→ What do I do on a regular day of life?

→ Where do I live? *Be specific.* Describe in detail your home, your surroundings, what it smells like, what colors are there. *All of it.*

→ What do you do for a living?

→ What do you wear? How do you take care of yourself?

Tips + Suggestions:

→ **Stay mindful and non-judgmental.** If you start to notice thoughts arise like, "there's no way that could happen," or "but how would I do that/have that," simply notice them, and let them go.

→ **Let this feel joyful.** It's your imagination. *Let it feel like play*!

date: _____

you may use the space below to write or choose to write on your computer.

WEEK ONE

WRITE *to* HEAL

day four:
self-perception

Today you are going to do a writing exercise designed to paint a more accurate representation of who you are.

There are four parts to this exercise.

You can review all four parts before beginning or take them one at a time. I invite you to look at my tips and suggestions for today's prompt, as you may find a gentle hug, encouragement, or motivation in them.

Tips & Suggestions:

→ **Try to be as honest with yourself as possible.** If you find yourself asking, "is this really how that person sees me, or am I inserting my own self-perception here?" it's likely that you are aware you're projecting some of your own self-perception.

→ **This exercise might be really difficult for a variety of reasons.** It can be saddening to read our self-description, as many of us are our worst critics. It can also be a reckoning of what we know to be true in our gut/heart about who we really are, and there may be resistance to admit that how we see ourselves isn't always how we're perceived by others.

→ **As much as you can, allow yourself to be willing and open to what you learn.** There can be a lot of resistance in changing our self-perception, as we often use it as a way to protect ourselves from perceived or feared criticism.

Part One: My perception.

Write a description of how you see yourself. This is both how you see yourself on the outside (physically) as well as on the inside. This might be difficult, or surprising. My invitation to you is be honest. Don't write how you *want* to see yourself, or how you once saw yourself. Write exactly as you see yourself, today.

Part Two: A loved one's perception.

Write a description of how your closest friends and family see you. Again, externally and internally. How would/do they describe you? What words/language do they use? If it helps, you can pick someone who loves you and knows you really well and write it as though it's from their perspective.

Part Three: A stranger's perception.

Write a description of how you think people might describe you after just meeting you for the first time. Try to resist the urge to insert your own self-perception here—be mindful of what you might be projecting around what a stranger might say vs. what you believe in your heart they might say about you.

Part Four: *Real Self.*

Using all three of these perceptions, where do you think the real you lies? What did you learn from using these three perspectives as a way to describe yourself? What would you like to change about your self-perception and the way you describe yourself?

day five:
hobbies, skills, & interests

Today's prompt is all about cultivating a sense of self *through our lifestyle.*

Oftentimes when we feel lost, disconnected, or fall out of love with life and living, it can be a reflection of not feeling grounded in activities and interests that bring us joy.

Having dedicated hobbies, interests, and skills fosters routine, provides the experience of growth and learning, and fuels our sense of connection, purpose, and joy. Many times, though, hobbies aren't born or innate! They are cultivated through routine, habit, and practice *before* they become enjoyable.

Today's Prompt: Hobbies, Skills, & Interests.

This prompt is meant to be done in list or table format. I'll explain below and have divided the next three pages up as a template if you'd like to use it in the workbook.

1. Use three separate sheets of paper. Divide each piece of paper into three columns (if you're using a computer, you can make a table or use a spreadsheet).
2. Label each column "Hobbies", "Interests," and "Skills".
3. The first page will be for past/previous hobbies, interests, and skills.
4. The second page will be for current hobbies, interests, and skills.
5. The last page will be for desired hobbies, interests, and skills, or ones you'd like to try.

Tips + Suggestions:

→ **Hobbies** can include anything you find or may find enjoyable, pleasurable, or stimulating! Hobbies include recreational sports, arts and crafts, literature and writing, music and theater (doing or watching), cooking, gardening, camping, tracking data, collecting...the list goes on!

→ **Interests** include anything you might be passionate about and can inform the ways you educate yourself/engage with learning, how you choose your social situations, or what you like to talk about. Interests might be certain academic subjects, people, time periods, objects, activities, religions, or anything you're generally fascinated by or curious about! *Allow this to be an opportunity to think more about what sparks your interest rather than something you might do.*

→ **Skills** include anything you're good at! You don't have to be an expert—it can simply be something you generally know how to do.

Past/Previous Hobbies, Skills, & Interests.

Hobbies	Skills	Interests

Current Hobbies, Skills, & Interests.

Hobbies	Skills	Interests

Desired Hobbies, Skills, & Interests.

Hobbies	Skills	Interests

day six:
letter from your older self

We often forget how wise we are, sitting in the dark wondering *what will I do next?*

How will I go on? What direction will I go? And will I make the wrong choice?

The answer, as much as we hope lives outside of us, does not. Its buried away in our gut. Left forgotten in our intuition. Stowed away, prepared to come out and offer its all-knowing wisdom, if we know how to access it.

So let's access it.

Today's Prompt: Write a letter *from your older self.*

Write a letter from your older self *as if it were being written to a grandchild or young person who is NOT you.* Imagine yourself at the end of your life—an age in which you've fully lived, and still have your mental capacities.

From this perspective, **complete the lead-ins on the next page** talking about life experiences you have *not yet* had. This is an exercise in imagination, as well as a tool to help us visualize a future we desire.

Tips & Suggestions:

→ **Let yourself use your imagination,** as most of these lead-ins are meant to elicit experiences you haven't lived yet!

→ **If you get stuck, close your eyes and picture yourself as an old, wise version of yourself.** Picture yourself sitting in a bright, warm room surrounded with soothing smells and sounds. Imagine yourself smiling, and imagine you are looked up to and respected. Speak and write from this place.

→ If certain lead-ins don't work, toss them! If you have your own lead-ins or ideas, go for it!

WEEK ONE

date: _____

you may use the space below to write or choose to write on your computer.

_____

Remember: You are completing these lead-ins as if you are an older version of yourself reflecting back on your life. It might help to write down what age you are writing from at the top of the page.

Some of my fondest memories in life include…

I have done a lot in my life. What I'm most proud of is…

There are also many things I'm not proud of. Some lessons I learned from mistakes I made are…

When things in life got hard, I picked myself back up by…

I'll never regret…

WEEK ONE

The people who mattered most to me were the ones who…

Once I did *this*, I suffered less….

If I could give my younger self one piece of advice, I would say…

What brought me more joy and peace than anything in my life was…

WRITE *to* HEAL

day seven:
reflect

Today all you'll be asked to do is reflect on the week of writing.

Sometimes, when we reflect on the work we've done, we are able to pull out nuggets of wisdom or seeds we want to plant that we weren't able to see during the process itself.

Today's Prompt: Reflect on *week one.*

Look back at this week of writing. Feel free to read what you wrote, or simply remind yourself of the prompts and what it felt like to reply to each. Write a reflection of this week of writing.

Here are some questions to consider to help you with your reflection:

→ What themes do you notice?

→ What have you learned?

→ What did you struggle with?

→ How do you feel different? (if you don't, that's ok!)

→ Did you write anything that sparked an idea you'd like to commit to?

→ What changes have you made in your daily life as a result of the writing?

Tips + Suggestions:

This is for you. Don't think of this as a prolific piece of writing—think of it as an opportunity to witness yourself as bystander.

WEEK ONE

date: _____

you may use the space below to write or choose to write on your computer.

WRITE *to* HEAL

week two

---

shedding.

Everything in life is a process of death and birth.
The hard part is letting death happen
so that we can create new life.

WRITE *to* HEAL

day eight:
defining moment

The theme of week two is unblocking, removing internal barriers, and healing old wounds.

You will spend time looking to the past this week. At times it may feel painful. At other times revelatory. The looking back won't last forever, and it's not necessary to do for long, or even at all if you don't want to. It is simply an invitation to deepen your self-awareness, to make sense of unconscious patterns, and perhaps invite freedom, softness, or the chance to let go of something that no longer needs a hold on you. My invitation this week is to find that softness. Be gentle. Go slow. Levity awaits.

Today's Prompt: Write about a *defining moment* in your life.

Imagine you are invited to speak at a TED Talk conference, where the subject is "defining moments." Write the speech you would make at a TED Talk about a defining moment in your life.

Here are some questions to consider to help you with your reflection:

→ What's a moment in my life I'll never forget?

→ What is an event that happened that changed how I saw myself or the world?

→ How am I different because of this moment?

→ What has changed in my life because of this event or experience?

→ What lesson did it teach me, and how can I impart that wisdom onto others?

Tips + Suggestions:

→ **If you've never seen a TED Talk,** take a moment to google "Ted Talk" and watch a short 1 to5 minute TED talk to get a feel for how they work.

→ **Use this as an opportunity to step into a leadership and authority role.** How can you write about your experience in a way that is powerful, inspiring, and engaging?

→ **Think about** *telling a story*—good stories have a beginning, middle, and end. Take your audience on a journey with this story.

Today's prompt may be a little hard to write.

I invite you to do this prompt when you have ample time to sit with the question and your response. If that means waiting until later in the day or even tomorrow, that's ok. Find a comfortable, quiet space where you feel safe, get grounded, and go slow.

date: _____

you may use the space below to write or choose to write on your computer.

WEEK TWO

WRITE *to* HEAL

day nine:
invisible

Ultimately, we all just want to be seen.

To know that we are real. To be acknowledged for our existence. And in the absence of our own reflection in others, we may struggle to believe that we are here at all.

Sometimes we aren't witnessed as children. We are ignored, dismissed, or shamed for who we are. For our expression. For feeling. We interpret these experiences as proof of our not-enoughness. Evidence that no matter how much we wave our personalities and brave the social world, we are not seen or accepted for who we really are. We become invisible then. As a way to protect ourselves we hide or fall quiet. Shrink and stay small. Or, believe we don't exist at all. This is a chance to re-*write* that wrong.

Today's Prompt: When did you feel *invisible?*

Think back on your childhood from the ages of about 4-13. Imagine a moment or moments when you felt utterly invisible. *What happened? Who was there? And what do you wish you could have said but didn't?*

Use this as an opportunity to re-write a moment in history, or to finally speak out/up in a moment when it was possibly unsafe or scary to have your voice be heard.

Your voice matters, and this is a practice of cultivating that voice by starting from the source, so that the courage you may not yet have to speak your truth can begin to flourish.

Here are some questions you can ask yourself:

→ When did I feel ignored?

→ When did I feel neglected?

→ When did I want to speak up about something, but felt unsafe/unallowed/scared to?

→ Why did I feel unsafe?

→ Who often made me feel invisible, and how?

→ If I could go back in time as a protective, wise older sibling, auntie, or mentor, how would I have helped my younger self? What might I have told myself or encouraged myself to say?

Tips + Suggestions:

→ **If you have serious trauma around the moment you've chosen,** I invite you to choose a less severe moment, UNLESS you have worked through this trauma in therapy already and feel safe to do so, OR if you can do this prompt with a therapist present.

→ The key components in this exercise are: **when** did I feel invisible, **who or what** instant made me feel invisible, and **what do I wish I could have said**/what would I like to say now to that person/people.

→ **Go slow, be gentle,** and if at any point you feel overwhelmed, panicked, distressed, or beginning to check out, please stop and return to the prompt when you feel grounded and calm.

→ Breathe. **You are not that person anymore.** You are here, now, and you have power, freedom, and autonomy. You have power.

date: _____

you may use the space below to write or choose to write on your computer.

WEEK TWO

WRITE *to* HEAL

day ten:
emerging

Chances are, if you're doing this workbook, you've felt the depths of darkness before.

And considering you're here, engaging with these prompts on the tenth day, you also have the will to pull yourself from the darkness. You have—despite what you may believe—tools and resources within you that encumber you with the strength or softness to get up and begin again.

Today, I'd like you to become more familiar with this part of you. I'd like you to go within and name these parts of self, so that if and when the darkness comes again, you have stark, clear images in your mind of the toolbox you already possess.

Today's Prompt: How I pulled myself *out of the dark.*

Think about a time in your life when you had to pull yourself out of the darkness. Maybe it was out of a depression, out of grief, out of heartbreak, loss, rejection, confusion...whatever the case. Write as if this were a chapter in a book, and the chapter was about "How I Pulled Myself Out of The Dark." Share what the low was, what it felt like, and what you did to come out of that place.

Tips + Suggestions

→ **If you have serious trauma around the moment you've chosen,** I invite you to choose a less severe moment, UNLESS you have worked through this trauma in therapy already and feel safe to do so, OR if you can do this prompt with a therapist present.

→ Think of this less as a "how to" and more of a deeply vulnerable and honest account of a difficult time, and the way you managed to find yourself again.

→ **Go slow, be gentle,** and if at any point you feel overwhelmed, panicked, distressed, or beginning to check out, please stop and return to the prompt when you feel grounded and calm.

→ If you find you'd rather have this framed more as a "how to," go for it! This is your story.

WEEK TWO

date: _____

you may use the space below to write or choose to write on your computer.

WRITE *to* HEAL

day eleven:
forgiveness

Once upon a time, I wanted to meet someone who had never made mistakes so I could be like them. Now, I want to meet someone who has never made mistakes so I might ask them, *why do you keep lying to us?*

Absence of error does not exist. What does exist is a culture of perfectionism—the absence of *admission* of error. The people I have met who seem flawless or whose histories seem pure and free from mistakes are not people living perfectly. They are simply people hiding their mistakes. I don't say this with judgment—we all hide our mistakes or our flaws. We minimize how we've hurt the ones we love. Disown parts of self we feel ashamed of, shoving them deep into our subconscious. *Why?* Fear. How terrifying it is to admit failure or fault in a room full of signs that scream, *I've never been dark like you.*

This is the paradox of living *truthfully*. To live *truthfully*, we have to admit fault, and to admit fault means standing naked and awkward in a room of clothed and polished. We must bear ourselves bravely until we feel safe in our imperfections, for the true danger lies in staying masked and afraid in a room full of pretenders.

To arrive at safety in imperfection, we have to acknowledge our error. We have to name our mistakes. And in doing so, we will undoubtably feel. This is often why we avoid naming our imperfectness. Because it hurts. It hurts our ego, it hurts our pride, or it hurts someone we love or even ourselves. If we don't acknowledge these hurts, though, we become identified with perfectionism or our ego-selves, and we only perpetuate the harm we hoped not to incite in the first place. We become one of the masked pretenders, crowding an already cold and disconnected space.

The work of finding safety in imperfection starts with feeling. Feeling, perhaps, guilt we didn't want to face for a mistake we made. Anger towards ourselves for being or acting a certain way. Disappointment, regret, or horror. When unprocessed, these feelings turn into shame. Shame becomes a cloak we wear if we aren't able to forgive ourselves—we interrupt guilt's erosion into shame with compassion. A witness. With forgiveness.

Today's Prompt: Write yourself a *letter of forgiveness.*

Think about a time/times in the past when you have not followed through on a promise to yourself, haven't completed a goal, self-sabotaged, or let yourself down.

Write the event/s in detail, describing what happened/didn't happen, how you felt, where you felt it in your body, what your thoughts were, how you treated yourself, and what the repercussions were.

Then, embody a loving, wise, higher inner self. From this space of deep compassion, wisdom, and understanding, *write yourself a letter of forgiveness.*

Tips + Suggestions:

→ **Remain as non-judgmental as possible.** Try not to re-criticize or re-judge yourself in the writing of the event. Write the event out as if you were a court stenographer, only writing what you see, hear, and observe without your feelings attached.

→ **Take a few minutes before writing your letter to visualize your higher self.** Maybe this is your wise inner parent, a spiritual self, or your older self. Someone and someplace where you can see your past self from a perspective that is loving, compassionate, and deeply understanding.

→ **Even if you have already forgiven your past self for any of these events, it will still benefit you to do this again.** Our brains create new pathways with repetition—*this is why patterns are so hard to break.* And, it's why when we want to cultivate new ways of being, repetition is our best friend.

WEEK TWO

date: _____

you may use the space below to write or choose to write on your computer.

WRITE to HEAL

day twelve:
dinner with my shadow

Shadow work may be a familiar concept to you. If it is, this will be a welcome challenge.

If you're new to shadow work, I invite you to see this exercise as a meet and greet with the parts of yourself you've cast away. A dinner party where you've invited your personality traits that irritate you, body parts that feel foreign to you, thought patterns that scare you, or behaviors that bother you.

Carl Jung describes the shadow as the repressed desires of the unconscious mind—parts of self we've shoved away for fear they won't be accepted, or worse, deemed evil or bad by our communities. These parts of self might arise in our dreams and be unknown to us in waking hours, or perhaps we are all too familiar with these parts as they have come out to play in drunken stupors or lashed out in fits of fury when we've "lost control" of our emotional world.

Shadow work comes in many forms, and if this feels important for you to investigate further, I invite you to look deeper into ways you can meet, greet, and learn to accept (and maybe even love) all that you are.

Today's Prompt: *Invite your shadow parts to dinner.*

Today I'd like you to make an invitation list for a dinner party, and the list includes your *shadow selves*. Your *shadow selves* are parts of yourself that you repress, feel ashamed of, or don't like.

The idea is to make an invitation list and *name* these parts of self. You'll first identify the part, then give it an actual, human name. You'll follow a set of prompts that will move you through the process of identifying, understanding, and hopefully, learning to accept and possibly love.

Tips + Suggestions:

→ **You can take this in any direction that feels helpful**—whether that means your parts of self are personality traits (like always making jokes in serious moments), emotions (like jealousy or rage), or behaviors (like getting too drunk at parties). *keep in mind, if you identify with any of the examples I just gave, I have zero judgment about you—these are examples of my own shadow self that I am practicing accepting and loving*

→ **Try to stay present with each question before making judgments or questioning the exercise.** It may feel strange to write out things you don't like about yourself. How can naming all that I *don't* love help me *love* myself? Trust the process, and allow yourself to be as honest and truthful as you can until the end.

→ **There is no right way to do this, nor is there a minimum or maximum number of parts to identify.** You can repeat this exercise any time in your life—in fact I encourage you to. There are parts of myself I am just now identifying as "shadow" parts that I never even knew existed several years ago. Focus on what is in your field of view today, and trust that these are the parts of you that need the most attention now.

date: _____

Part One: The Invite List.

Make a list of all your "shadow selves." To get you in the headspace, think about this question: *If I were to attend a dinner party, what parts of myself would I like to leave at home? What parts of myself would I be embarrassed to bring with me?*

Your list can be written as "the part of me that…" or "my tendency to…" or "my…" or whatever feels right. I've made space for five parts, but you can do more or less.

For each part of self, you'll follow specific prompts. I've set aside five pages to use for five different parts of self—you can do more, or you can do less.

You can use the pages here, or in your own journal or laptop.

Extra invitation: Give your part of self a name. See how that shifts your perception, and how.

Part of Self: _____ Name it: _____

What I don't like about this part of me:

How this part of me hurts myself:

How this part of me hurts others:

How this part of me helps me:

How this part of me helps others:

Why I need this part of me:

Why I love this part of me:

Part of Self: _____Name it: _____

What I don't like about this part of me:

How this part of me hurts myself:

How this part of me hurts others:

How this part of me helps me:

How this part of me helps others:

Why I need this part of me:

Why I love this part of me:

Part of Self: _____Name it: _____

What I don't like about this part of me:

How this part of me hurts myself:

How this part of me hurts others:

How this part of me helps me:

How this part of me helps others:

Why I need this part of me:

Why I love this part of me:

Part of Self: _____Name it: _____

What I don't like about this part of me:

How this part of me hurts myself:

How this part of me hurts others:

How this part of me helps me:

How this part of me helps others:

Why I need this part of me:

Why I love this part of me:

Part of Self: _____ Name it: _____

What I don't like about this part of me:

How this part of me hurts myself:

How this part of me hurts others:

How this part of me helps me:

How this part of me helps others:

Why I need this part of me:

Why I love this part of me:

WRITE *to* HEAL

day thirteen:
safety

Safety and security are our two most basic, fundamental human needs. And yet, so many of us feel utterly unsafe—in our bodies, in our environments, or in our relationships.

Today is all about harnessing safety for yourself so that as you move forward in life, you have more awareness around what you need to feel safe in order to *truly be you* outside of the small circle of safety that is known. We must learn to create safety in ourselves and know what we need to feel safe outside of our known environments so that we can brave the unknown.

This doesn't mean living fearlessly—it means having faith that even if something is unfamiliar, we are safe to try something new. We are safe to be ourselves before we know if we are liked. We are safe to voice our desires and needs even if it's uncertain they will be met.

Today's Prompt: *What does safety mean to me?*

Today I'm inviting you to reflect on the concept of safety, and your relationship (or lack of) to it. Oftentimes when we have a history of trauma, we feel unsafe in situations that are inherently safe. We may experience social anxiety, discomfort in our own bodies, or constantly believing the worst will happen. Today's prompt will help you clarify ways you can cultivate *more* safety in your life so you can actually engage with your life, and hopefully learn that those situations that once felt unsafe are not here anymore, and it is safe for you to live and be in the world.

Here are some questions to ask yourself if you're not sure where to start:

→ How do you know you are safe?

→ What kinds of people make you feel safe?

→ What kinds of places make you feel safe?

→ What practices and behaviors do you engage in that make you feel safe?

→ How do you gauge what is/isn't safe in your life so that you know its ok for you to move forward with an endeavor, conversation, or relationship?

Tips + Suggestions:

→ **If you have no idea what makes you feel safe,** you can try and start with what makes you feel unsafe. Using this, you can imagine what the opposite of that might be.

→ **Safety isn't just physical.** Safety also can be how we feel in our body, how we feel about our belief system, and the security we feel in our sense of self. Try using this perspective as well as the physical.

date: _____

you may use the space below to write or choose to write on your computer.

WEEK TWO

WRITE *to* HEAL

day fourteen:
reflect

Darling, you've just completed two weeks of writing and deep connection to self.

Today all you'll be asked to do is reflect on the week of writing. Sometimes, when we reflect on the work we've done, we are able to pull out nuggets of wisdom or seeds we want to plant that we weren't able to see in the process itself.

Today's Prompt: Reflect on *week two.*

Look back at this week of writing. Feel free to read what you wrote, or simply remind yourself of the prompts and what it felt like to reply to each. Write a reflection of this week of writing.

Here are some questions to consider to help you with your reflection:

→ What themes do you notice?

→ What have you learned?

→ What did you struggle with?

→ How do you feel different? (if you don't, that's ok!)

→ Did you write anything that sparked an idea you'd like to commit to?

→ What changes have you made in your daily life as a result of the writing?

Tips + Suggestions:

This is for you. Don't think of this as a prolific piece of writing—think of it as an opportunity to witness yourself as an outside bystander.

WEEK TWO

date: _____

you may use the space below to write or choose to write on your computer.

WRITE *to* HEAL

week three.

---

planting.

I died, once.

It didn't hurt like I thought it might. In fact, I felt relieved. What hurt was what came next. The part when I had to start growing new bones from scratch. The part when I had to burst through the soil while still young and vulnerable. The part where I saw the sun for the first time again, and its brightness burned me.

When it came time to die again, it was not the death I feared. It was the starting over.

With each death, though, I learned something new. I learned that if I shape my arms just so, I could puncture the earth with less effort. I know which direction to face to soak up the most sunlight. I know how to bend and fold with the wind so I don't break, I bend.

Planting doesn't scare me anymore, because I learned how to garden.

WRITE *to* HEAL

day fifteen:
one small step

We can sit at the water's edge admiring the horizon all we like, but the only way we'll know what lies on the other side is by getting in.

Just as we can't expect ourselves to traverse the ocean's vastness in one stroke, we cannot expect to arrive at a goal or dream in one step. We have to take each step to get there. We have to make each stroke to cross the water.

Today you'll start to get clear on what those first steps are—not the overarching plan, not the entire rubric, not the end—just the steps you can take today to move in the direction you've envisioned.

Today's Prompt: How can I take *one small step* towards my life?

Take a moment to reflect on some of the discoveries you had from week one and two. You wrote about your dream future, visualized yourself as an elder and imparted wisdom, and maybe tapped into some wounds from the past or patterns that are keeping you stuck.

What is one *practical* step you can take today towards your dream life that both honors *and* challenges some of the roadblocks you may experience in your life situation?

Tips + Suggestions:

→ **This is not necessarily meant to be a roadmap** or full guide for how to get to your dream life. This is about one, small, actionable step you can take that moves you in that direction, and one that keeps in mind what you've learned about yourself in the writing process.

→ Once you identify what you can do, **write about it as if you are actually doing it**—describe the steps you're taking, where you are, what it sounds/smells like, who is there, and how you feel.

→ If you are able to, try and actually do the thing!

WEEK THREE

date: _____

you may use the space below to write or choose to write on your computer.

WRITE *to* HEAL

day sixteen:
values

We all have a set of values that we live by, whether we are aware of them or not.

Sometimes these are values we've chosen consciously—a code of ideals we aim to live by in order to feel aligned and in integrity with who we are and what matters to us. Other times, we inherit family or social values which subconsciously start to run our life.

If you've ever felt obligated to live in a way that doesn't feel right, you may be operating from a set of values that simply aren't yours. It's also possible that you're operating from values that you've outgrown. Maybe you did values work several years ago, but since then you've changed jobs, relationships, or experienced a major life event. Whatever the case, we change with time, and so do our values.

It's crucial that we find some clarity and connection to our values so that we can move about life in a way that feels aligned. Values don't just inform how we act or spend our time—they also support us in creating boundaries, preserving energy, and letting go. If we choose to enter into any kind of leadership role, sturdy, clear values support us in keeping a steady foot. As we extend our beliefs, thoughts, and gifts out into a world that undoubtably will challenge, disagree, or question us, having a solid value base can help.

The idea is not to have such rigid values that we cannot be swayed—rather the idea is to be clear on your boundaries so that you can stay focused and mindful *while* being open to new ideas (unless, of course, rigidity is a value of yours. Herein lies personal freedom.)

Today's Prompt: Identify *four-five* core values.

This is a simple exercise that I have used for many years. You'll see a list of value statements (words) below. You'll start by circling (or writing down) any words/values that resonate with you. Then, you'll go through and organize the words you've chosen into categories—for example if you circle compassion, kindness, and empathy, those likely would go into the same category. Once you've done this, try to narrow your categories down to four or five major themes. Select the word from each theme that best represents each category, and you'll have your core values.

Tips + Suggestions:

→ **First thought best thought.** For the first round of choosing words, try not to filter or question yourself. If a word resonates, circle it. Once you go back and put words into categories, you may notice that some words don't align as much as others.

→ **If you're not sure if a word is *your* value or adopted from someone else,** ask yourself "have I ever been told this *should* matter to me?" "Why does this feel important to me?" "If this was a value, how would it make me behave, and would I like that about myself?" "Who else do I know that has this value?"

→ **You can always come back to this exercise.** If you go through this workbook and think, "hmm, I think those values I set are actually a little off," that's ok! You can revisit this prompt at any time.

Values List

Acceptance	Community	Empower	Harmony
Accountability	Compassion	Endurance	Health
Accuracy	Competence	Energy	Honesty
Achievement	Concentration	Enjoyment	Honor
Adaptability	Confidence	Enthusiasm	Hope
Alertness	Connection	Equality	Humility
Altruism	Consciousness	Ethical	Humor
Ambition	Consistency	Excellence	Imagination
Amusement	Contentment	Experience	Improvement
Assertiveness	Contribution	Exploration	Independence
Attentive	Control	Fairness	Individuality
Awareness	Conviction	Family	Innovation
Balance	Cooperation	Famous	Inquisitive
Beauty	Courage	Fearless	Insightful
Boldness	Creativity	Feelings	Inspiring
Bravery	Credibility	Ferocious	Integrity
Brilliance	Curiosity	Fidelity	Intelligence
Calm	Decisive	Focus	Intensity
Candor	Decisiveness	Foresight	Intuitive
Capable	Dedication	Fortitude	Joy
Careful	Dependability	Freedom	Justice
Certainty	Determination	Friendship	Kindness
Challenge	Development	Fun	Knowledge
Charity	Devotion	Generosity	Lawful
Cleanliness	Dignity	Genius	Leadership
Clear	Discipline	Giving	Learning
Clever	Discovery	Grace	Liberty
Comfort	Drive	Gratitude	Logic
Commitment	Effectiveness	Greatness	Love
Common sense	Efficiency	Growth	Loyalty
Communication	Empathy	Happiness	Mastery

Maturity	Results-oriented	Talent
Meaning	Reverence	Teamwork
Moderation	Rigor	Temperance
Motivation	Risk	Thankful
Openness	Satisfaction	Thorough
Optimism	Security	Thoughtful
Organization	Self-reliance	Timeliness
Originality	Selfless	Tolerance
Passion	Sensitivity	Toughness
Patience	Serenity	Traditional
Peace	Service	Tranquility
Performance	Sharing	Transparency
Persistence	Significance	Trust
Playfulness	Silence	Trustworthy
Poise	Simplicity	Truth
Potential	Sincerity	Understanding
Power	Skill	Uniqueness
Present	Skillfulness	Unity
Productivity	Smart	Valor
Professionalism	Solitude	Victory
Prosperity	Spirituality	Vigor
Purpose	Spontaneous	Vision
Quality	Stability	Vitality
Realistic	Status	Wealth
Reason	Stewardship	Welcoming
Recognition	Strength	Winning
Recreation	Structure	Wisdom
Reflective	Success	Wonder
Respect	Support	
Responsibility	Surprise	
Restraint	Sustainability	

WRITE *to* HEAL

date: _____

you may use the space below to write or choose to write on your computer.

WEEK THREE

WRITE *to* HEAL

day seventeen: *soften*

How you show up for yourself will inform how you show up for others.

Unfortunately, we often extend such kindness to those around us and neglect our own emotional and physical needs. We are soft and gentle with those in our presence, yet harsh and unforgiving towards ourselves.

To lead with courage is to lead by example. Who am I to teach self-compassion if I don't myself practice it? How could I understand the challenges that come with self-kindness if I don't face that challenge myself? How could I entertain the questions people may ask around loving themselves, if I do not know in my body the experience of relating to my own inner world?

Today you are going to set yourself up for times when softening and self-compassion may not come so readily. When you may feel an urge to err on the side of self-hatred or self-harm. Or when subtle thoughts of not-enoughness or urgency creep in, and you need a swift reminder *that you are doing just fine.*

Today's Prompt: Write 10 affirmations *for softness.*

Today, I'd like you to make a list of 10 affirmations you can use in any time or moment when you need a little softness.

I've done one below to give you an example:

I have the capacity to do great things—and one of the greatest things I can do is be gentle with myself.

Tips + Suggestions:

→ Think about how you might write an affirmation for a young, innocent child who is being hard on themselves.

→ Words like "softness, tender, gentle, kind" can stir up the sentiment we are going for, so feel free to use those words as starting points.

→ If you get stuck, think about what a great compassionate leader might say. How would the Dalai Lama speak softly to you?

date: _____

you may use the space below to write or choose to write on your computer.

1.

2.

3.

4.

5.

6.

8.

9.

10.

day eighteen:
finding your voice

An energy healer once said to me, "Rachel, when you feel like you are choking, it is not because you holding back tears. It is because you are choking on the words you have swallowed whole for 30 years."

When I was a little girl, I was very quiet. I was sensitive, curious, and observant. These are traits I now love about myself. Still, this natural noticing quality was one that eventually muted me. People expected me to stay quiet, so they didn't ask my opinion. People assumed I had nothing to say, so they spoke around me or over me. People assumed my silence was stupidity, so when I did finally speak, they didn't wait for me to finish before injecting their voices. I learned to stay quiet, *when what I should have learned was to stay curious.* I learned to stay silent, *when what I should have learned was to be loud if and when I chose.* I learned I was stupid, *when what I should have learned is that wisdom is not measured in airtime.*

It took years for me to learn to speak up. Years for me to feel comfortable saying, "I haven't finished speaking yet." Years, still, for me to feel confident and safe enough in my body and convictions to say, "I disagree, this is what I think."

Once I came to realize my voice had a place in this world—and not in a way that polarized or denied the other—but in a way where I could offer my ideas, opinions, or questions without swallowing my words, I found more freedom in every other aspect of myself, my relationships, and my life.

Today's Prompt: *How do I find my voice?*

I'd like you to think about a situation in your life where you felt as if you should have held an opinion but didn't. This can be as mundane as "what's your favorite ice cream," or as complex as "where do you stand on XYZ politically." Write an inquiry around why you didn't feel like you had an opinion, how you felt about not having a stance, and perhaps other times in your life where you've felt disconnected from a personal standpoint.

From this place, allow yourself to write out what your opinions might be, or what you might need to do in order to formulate one.

Tips + Suggestions:

This is not about finding polarity or getting so firm on a subject matter that you're unable to see things from another perspective—this is about finding some sense of personal philosophy and belief, likes and dislikes, and a general compass for how you individually see and direct yourself in the world.

WRITE *to* HEAL

date: _____

you may use the space below to write or choose to write on your computer.

WEEK THREE

WRITE *to* HEAL

day nineteen:
speak your truth

Today you're going to speak your truth. You're going to use writing as a vehicle to say something you've been wanting to say, but perhaps have been too scared to.

Often, we are afraid to speak our truth because of perceived judgment, criticism, or shame. Other times we fear who we might hurt with our words, or who we might lose by speaking our truth.

Today, the invitation is to write as freely and truly as you can, *knowing only you will see what you've written.* The first step in facing that fear is *simply allowing yourself to have a voice.* The more you do this, the more you will find courage, strength, and wisdom to speak your truth *no matter who is listening.*

Today's Prompt: *What story are you afraid to tell?*

Today I am going to let you take a little more control over the circumstances of this piece. I'll give you some possible suggestions to help you get started, and, ultimately, this prompt is all about sharing a story you have in your heart without holding back.

Here are some ideas if you don't already know what that story might be:

→ **Think of a time when you didn't stand up for yourself, but wish you had.** What happened? Who was there? What have you learned since then, and what do you wish you could have done or said?

→ What is something that has happened in your life that you believe **would be healing for others to read about?**

→ If you were really honest with the world about how you felt, what might you say?

→ Imagine you could share a story or experience, and **your parents/caregivers would never read it or hear about it.** *What story would you tell?*

Tips + Suggestions:

→ **If you choose a story or event that was traumatic,** I invite you to go very, very slow, and process the writing with a therapist or support person if you have one.

→ Remember, **no one will *ever* read this** *unless you want them to.* You can even write this and then burn it if you like. The point is not necessarily to put this out into the world. Rather to give yourself permission to freely write, express, and process the event as if you had full freedom to tell this story.

→ **Be bold. Dig deep.** This is your moment to be courageous without consequence. This is the time to be honest. Brutally transparent. *Open yourself up to the page.*

date: _____

you may use the space below to write or choose to write on your computer.

WEEK THREE

WRITE *to* HEAL

day twenty:
patterns

Self-acceptance and self-compassion matter *not* because they absolve us from change, but rather because they offer us the kindness and encouragement required to let go of what no longer serves us and try something different.

I spent countless hours in counseling staring angrily at my therapist. She was adamant that if I wanted to stop binge-eating and drinking, all I would have to do was be kind to myself when I did. "But Ama," I would argue, "I don't want to do it in the first place. Why do you keep telling me to be nice to myself when I do it, instead of telling me how to *stop doing it?*" She never did tell me how. She just looked at me sideways, like a puzzled puppy, as if I was missing the point altogether.

I wasn't missing the point. At least, not in the moment. I understood that beating myself up or yelling at myself wasn't going to prevent me from engaging in behaviors I wanted to stop. That would be like suggesting I self-harm in order to stop self-harming. That makes no sense. The point I *was missing* was that in order to *create new patterns*, I would need a reason more loving and kinder than *because I hate myself*. I was still trying to make changes *based on the belief that I was worthless*. As long as my motivator was coming from a place of self-hatred, I was never going to successfully change the patterns.

Patterns of behavior are extensions of patterns of thought—what motivates us informs how we act. If I wanted to *stop* doing things that hurt me, I had to *start* thinking about myself as someone I didn't want to hurt.

Today's Prompt: Patterns of past, and *patterns of change.*

Today's prompt will ask you to gently examine patterns of behavior in your life that you are hoping *to change, transform,* or *let go of.* This is not about shaming, nor is it about *not* accepting yourself as you are, fully. This is about bringing awareness to ways we self-sabotage, self-harm, or act out unresolved trauma that feels out of alignment with our values and who we know we are.

You will need to make a table for this prompt. I have done so for you on the following pages if you want to use this book, or you can use the instructions below to make your own.

INSTRUCTIONS:

Make three columns on your piece of paper. The left-hand column will be labeled **"Patterns"**, the middle column will be labeled **"Precipitating Event,"** and the third column will be labeled **"Alternatives."**

In the left-hand column titled "Patterns," I want you (with a lot of kindness and self-compassion), to list any patterns of behavior you have that you are hoping to change. This can be things like compulsive eating, skin-picking, procrastinating, staying up late, smoking, lashing out, avoiding confrontation, etc. The behaviors can be small or big—it's up to you.

In the middle column titled "Alternatives," think about any events that seem to be common threads that happen BEFORE the pattern behavior. This may require some honest self-reflection, hard thinking, and honesty. For example, I binge-eat, and it usually happens after I feel rejected in some capacity. It's not always exactly the same, nor is it always RIGHT before the binge-eat. And, I can usually trace a binge-eat to a recent rejection of some sort.

Finally, on the right-hand column "Precipitating Event", make 1-2 ideas for alternative behaviors. Try to be realistic and kind—it may be very hard to jump straight from binge-eating to meditation. A smaller step might be "make an intentional snack, and journal about my feelings" or "make a cup of tea and text my therapist." Allowing it to be more of a side-step than a 180 may lead to greater likelihood of trying the alternative.

Tips + Suggestions

→ **Be so, so gentle.** This is not an exercise meant to judge, shame, or criticize yourself. It is meant to help you gain some awareness and insight and get curious about how and why some of these patterns exist in your life.

→ **Even if you already know WHY** you have some of these patterns, it's still helpful to write this out and see it on paper.

→ **If you can't trace down a precipitating event,** try asking yourself, "the last time this happened, what was I doing right beforehand? If I HADN'T engaged in the pattern behavior, how might I have been feeling?"

→ Notice I am not calling these "problem" behaviors. Nothing you are doing is a problem, unless you are a serious harm to yourself or others.

Even then, I don't consider you or the behavior a problem, I would instead frame that as you struggling immensely and having developed a technique to soothe you that has become so familiar that the idea of trying something else is terrifying.

You are not bad. You are not broken. You are human. And, sometimes these patterns hurt us just as much as the precipitating event, and its ok to want to seek another way to comfort yourself.

WRITE *to* HEAL

date:_____

Pattern   **Alternatives**   **Precipitating Event**

day twenty-one:
reflect

Darling, you've just completed three weeks of writing and deep connection to self.

Today all you'll be asked to do is reflect on the week of writing. Sometimes, when we reflect on the work we've done, we are able to pull out nuggets of wisdom or seeds we want to plant that we weren't able to see in the process itself.

Today's Prompt: Reflect on *week three.*

Look back at this week of writing. Feel free to read what you wrote, or simply remind yourself of the prompts and what it felt like to reply to each. Write a reflection of this week of writing.

Here are some questions to consider to help you with your reflection:

→ What themes do you notice?

→ What have you learned?

→ What did you struggle with?

→ How do you feel different? (if you don't, that's ok!)

→ Did you write anything that sparked an idea you'd like to commit to?

→ What changes have you made in your daily life as a result of the writing?

Tips + Suggestions:

This is for you. Don't think of this as a prolific piece of writing—think of it as an opportunity to witness yourself as an outside bystander.

WEEK THREE

date: _____

you may use the space below to write or choose to write on your computer.

WRITE *to* HEAL

week four.

---

garden.

I started cutting roses from my garden
not because I wanted to watch something die
but because I wanted to see
the look on your face
when I handed them to you.

WRITE *to* HEAL

day twenty-two:
what stands out

When we plant seeds, we can have some level of certainty around what we are growing.

What we can't know, though, is the direction they will grow. It is our job as the gardener to, as my therapist says, *hold loosely* the vision of our plant. Hold the vision of what you've planted, and pay close attention to what unexpectedly sprouts as in the process.

Today's Prompt: *What stands out from all I've written?*

Today, you will start to pay attention to how your seed is growing. You will observe themes, trends, or new ideas that have started forming that perhaps you didn't expect or plan for.

Look back at all of the writing you've done in this workbook and **choose one prompt or answer that stands out the most to you.** Write a reflection of this prompt and what it stirred in you.

Here are some questions to consider to help with your reflection:

→ What about that prompt/reply felt impactful?

→ What did you learn from this prompt?

→ Is there a story in this answer that you could tell?

→ Who else might be impacted by this prompt or your reply, and how could your reflection help them?

WEEK FOUR

date: _____

you may use the space below to write, or choose to write on your computer.

WRITE *to* HEAL

day twenty-three:
who needs my story?

It's not the story you say that matters—it's *how you tell the story*, and *who you tell it to.*

For years I contemplated writing about my eating disorder. I battled with myself, asking, *why would anyone care about my life,* and, *who am I to talk about my illness if I'm not even well?* Once I found the courage to actually write, the self-doubt thickened, and I started to believe that because I hadn't been through *as much* trauma or been *as sick* as other eating disorder patients, I didn't have the right to share my story.

There was validity to my internal dialogue—the trauma I've faced is not even a fraction of what millions have endured, and as a white, cis-passing, straight-bodied woman from a middle-class family, my privilege allotted me far more resources and protection than others, and continues to do so.

Still, my story matters. Because regardless of our past or present, our collective wellness is a reflection of our individual wellness. And someone who sees themselves in my story, who undoubtably might have the same privilege or access to care as me, still deserves to feel less alone and find health so that they can play a positive role in the fabric of society. Sickness is not isolated. It's contagious. So is health. So is love. So is connection.

There will always be someone who has suffered more. There will always be someone who has more peace. Still, there is power in sharing the path I'm on, so that someone who sees themselves in me can know they're not alone in the walking.

Today's Prompt: Write a character description of *the one who needs my story.*

When you think about the healing you've done, are doing, or want to do, think about who might benefit from hearing your journey. Write a character description of this person. Even if you don't plan on writing a book, think of this as an opportunity to imagine how you might pass on wisdom to a child, a student, or the generation below you.

Here are some questions to consider to help with your reflection:

→ How old is this person?

→ What are they struggling with?

→ Where do they live? With whom?

→ What have they experienced in their lives?

→ What are their dreams and goals?

→ What are their fears?

→ What kind of mentor or wise person would they listen to? What qualities would that person have? What would they want to learn from them?

→ How does this person feel loved and supported?

Tips + Suggestions

→ Rather than focusing on how you could help this person, **focus on** *who* **this person is and** *what they need.*

→ Maybe you'll find this person is a younger version of yourself, that's perfectly ok!

→ **Paint a picture.** Be descriptive. Heck, draw the person if you want! The more detail, the better.

→ Worry less about *why* you are doing this exercise and focus more on *doing it.*

WEEK FOUR

date: _____

you may use the space below to write or choose to write on your computer.

WRITE *to* HEAL

day twenty-four:
what I wish they knew

Today we will start to pull back the veil of vulnerability. Today we open the windows for our deepest desires—not the ones we dream of for our self, but perhaps the one we dream of for humanity. For our past self. For generations to come.

Suffering exposes us to dark edges we never imagined existed. It's in these dark places we come to learn what's missing. It's in these dark places we come to learn what needs light. So what needs light? What do those who haven't seen the darkness miss? What could others glean from your wisdom in the trenches, so that they can shine a light in the right places, from a good distance, and with enough light to help those who find themselves buried below feel safe to come out?

Today's Prompt: *What do I wish people knew about mental health?*

When it comes to mental health (either your own or as a concept in general) what do you wish people knew? Write down, as if you were giving an honest, inspirational speech to the masses about mental health, exactly what you would want the world to know. **If the concept of mental health doesn't align, you can replace it with something else that holds meaning for you.**

Here are some questions to consider to help with your reflection:

→ What does mental health mean to you? How would you explain it to someone?

→ What do you wish was normalized?

→ What do you wish was better understood?

→ What do you wish was different?

→ What do you think is most important for people to know?

→ How do you think this could change the world for the better?

→ Why do you think these things aren't known?

→ How can you approach this message and topic in a way that will reach your audience?

Tips + Suggestions

→ Think about inspiring, educating, and connecting with your words.

→ **Try using metaphors, stories, or personal anecdotes** to connect the audience with your message to make it personal.

→ How can you impart this important message without othering the reader or making them feel helpless?

date: _____

you may use the space below to write or choose to write on your computer.

WEEK FOUR

WRITE *to* HEAL

day twenty-five:
what would you teach

Whether you hope to use what you discover in this workbook to write, create, or lead, you will likely find that those who read your work are students. We learn from art. We learn from words. We learn from exposure—that which is placed before us becomes a novelty that our brains attempt to decipher, and we absorb and inherit the information like a sponge.

Even music is a teacher: it shows our bodies how to move with rhythm. It massages our mind, teaching our neural pathways to relax and rest.

Your work will have power, and that comes with responsibility. Whether you intend to or not, you will teach. Regardless of your *how*, I'm going to invite you to get curious about what your role might be as someone passing on wisdom.

Today's Prompt: If I could get paid to teach anything I wanted, *what would I teach?*

Imagine you were a teacher, and you were offered a salary that would pay all your bills to teach anything you wanted. What would you teach? How would you teach it?

Write an outline as if you were going to conduct a several week-long course. Identify themes for each week, a progression of learning, and an overall structure.

Here are some questions to help you get started:

→ **The sky is the limit.** Educate in a way that feels meaningful.

→ How do you wish you had been taught? **Not what, but *how?***

→ What **lessons** would you teach, specifically? And in what order?

→ **How long** would it take you to teach what you wanted to teach?

→ What major lesson is taught each week?

→ How would you measure your student's progress?

→ What would your mission statement be?

→ What are your **boundaries** as an educator?

WEEK FOUR

date: _____

you may use the space below to write or choose to write on your computer.

WRITE *to* HEAL

day twenty-six:
the "leader" self

Many therapeutic techniques invite us to name a part of self in order to strengthen personal characteristics.

We can use these tools in a variety of ways, and I find it helpful to externalize and personify parts of myself, especially when it's a part of myself I'm hoping to strengthen.

By thinking of parts of self as external systems that we have relationships to and with, we support ourselves in remaining unidentified with one way of being. Sometimes when we step into new roles (life partner, CEO, parent, student) we mistakenly *identify* with that role, which can actually create dysfunction or loss of self. What happens if we drop, change, or let go of that role? Who are we without it? It's vital to our essence of being to witness our roles in life (this goes for diagnoses, too) as parts of self or external from self, rather than *the self.* When I was in Eating Disorder recovery, I realized I had become so identified with my Eating Disorder that getting well actually meant losing my identity altogether.

We are multifaceted, and to remain multifaceted its helpful to become aware of and in good relationship with those facets.

Think of your "leader self" as one of those facets: a part of self that knows how to step up, provide direction, guide, and organize. Today you are going to get more familiar with your leader self so that if and when the time comes, you know how to draw on these skills, traits, and perspectives to effectively lead *without* becoming identified with *being* a leader.

Today's Prompt: Write a character description of yourself *as a leader.*

Today I'd like you to get really clear on your "leader self." This is similar to visualizing a higher self, wise self, inner parent, or elder self. **You are going to write in detail what the leadership version of you is like** so that you know exactly how to embody this role when you are ready.

If you were a leader of any kind—whether leading the charge for a friend's birthday party or guiding thousands of people through social change, *how would you lead?*

Here are some questions to answer/consider:

→ What would your mission or philosophy as a leader be?
→ What do you think makes a good leader? A bad leader?
→ How would you speak to people?
→ How would you address mistakes, error, or not having answers?
→ What would be your ethics or values as a leader?
→ What would your boundaries be within the container of this role?
→ What would the leader-version of you be doing on a daily basis?

Tips + Suggestions

→ Imagine yourself as the leader you *want to be.*

→ If you find yourself thinking "I wouldn't be a good leader because..." ask yourself, "how would a good leader respond to this kind of internal dialogue?" *How do good leaders deal with their own insecurities?*

→ Ask yourself *not* what you would need to change to be a good leader, *but what you already possess that makes you one.*

→ What qualities do you think make someone ELSE a good leader? How could you embody those?

WEEK FOUR

date: _____

you may use the space below to write or choose to write on your computer.

WRITE *to* HEAL

day twenty-seven:
chapter one

Today I am going to challenge you to write something *slightly* cohesive.

Don't worry, I am not asking you to show this to anyone or ever use it—I am, however, inviting you to write as if you were. To seriously put pen to page and construct *what could be* a first chapter in the book of *you*.

Today's Prompt: *Write the first chapter of your book.*

Imagine you were writing a book. It could be about anything—your life, someone else's topic you are passionate about, or even a fiction novel with a story from your imagination. *What would chapter one be?*

Write the first chapter in that book.

Tips + Suggestions

→ **Let this be play.** Don't worry about it being perfect or well written or even making sense. Drop into a state of childlike wonder, imagination, and flow.

→ **You can first think of what your book or even chapter might be called** (again, this is just for fun, nothing has to stick or be real) to help stir up some ideas for a chapter one.

→ If you have been feeling called to write a book already and have been imagining your first chapter for a while, **this could be the kickstart to beginning.**

→ **Don't self-edit.** Let this be a brain-dump. Write without self-editing during the process. Let it just be a "I'm dumping whatever I can onto a page right now."

→ If you feel *really* stuck, try writing a chapter in a children's picture book!

WEEK FOUR

date: _____

you may use the space below to write or choose to write on your computer.

WRITE *to* HEAL

day twenty-eight:
the final chapter

All great storytelling has a beginning, a middle, and an end.

Sometimes we are able to *start* the story with ease. Other times we know what the *meat* of the story is, but struggle to know where the story starts and how we get to the juicy middle. More often than not, it's the endings that are most puzzling for creatives—our minds have so many beginnings, and loose ends trail behind us like popped balloons.

Sometimes it's helpful to know how it ends before it begins. Think of this as creating your destination—an arrival point for the art or writing you are creating, a vision to hold, an end point in sight.

Today's Prompt: Write the last chapter in *the book of your life.*

Imagine you were writing a book about a part of your life. It can be a part of your life that has already ended, or hasn't.

Write the last chapter *in that book.*

Tips + Suggestions

→ **Don't worry about this being the actual ending for a book.** Instead focus on how you could write an ending that felt like it had closure, a message, and a period of resolve.

→ **Think about how you would feel reading your story.** What would make you feel complete to read at the end?

→ What are some ways **other people end stories** that you enjoy?

→ **Remember—hold this loosely.** Use this as an exercise for finding comfort in an eventual landing point, rather than a stake in the ground as to how this all must end.

WEEK FOUR

date: _____

you may use the space below to write or choose to write on your computer.

WRITE *to* HEAL

day twenty-nine:
mission statement

Many great leaders have solid *whys*. They are less concerned with the *what*, because *what* they create and *how* remains flexible when their *why* is solid.

Whether you intend to use what you've discovered in this workbook to write a book, create art, teach, or find more clarity in your professional world, now is the time to solidify your *why*, and use that to inform your *mission statement*.

A mission statement is a mantra or philosophy that drives all that you plant and grow. It will allow you, time and time again, to remain focused and return to center if and when you become distracted, overwhelmed, or caught in comparison. When we are clear on our *why*, the work, relationships, or experiences we create from that core blossom with vibrant ease. *My mission statement: To make one person feel less alone.*

Today's Prompt: What is your *why?*

Using the line of questioning below, you'll get clear on your core *why*. Once your why feels clear, use what you discover to formulate a simple, singular phrase that can be used as a mission statement.

Tips + Suggestions

→ **First thought best thought.** As you move through the questions, worry less about having a perfect/right answer, and more about what comes first to your mind (or body). This is an intuitive process, as we are hoping to get to the core of your why.

→ **You can always go through this process again.** If you do this exercise today and find that you don't feel very connected to the *why* or mission statement you come up with, that's ok. Revisit it in a few days and see if anything new arises.

→ **Try to commit to a mission statement.** Once you find a *why* that feels true, and once you write a mission statement, commit. The more we remain consistent in the seed we plant, the healthier the garden we grow.

→ **Listen to your emotions.** You'll essentially ask yourself "why" until you *feel* something. When I last did this exercise, I thought I knew my *why*. But as my assistant asked me to unpack each *why* further and further, I realized I wasn't emotionally connected to the original idea, until one answer I provided made me cry. *"Oh,"* I thought, *"this is it. This is why I do what I do."*

176

→ **Try to stick with** *you.* If you notice yourself answering each question with "because other people XYZ…" bring it back to self. Why does other people doing/not knowing/acting in a certain way matter *to you?*

date: _____

you may use the space below to write, or choose to write on your computer.

_____

Why do you want to [insert doing what you are doing]?
Example: "why do you want to write a book?" *or* "why do you want to make content about relationships?"

Why is that important to you?

And why is *that* important to you?

Why? (you see the picture—you'll essentially ask "why" to each answer, until your gut says "oh, this is *why*."

WEEK FOUR

WRITE *to* HEAL

day thirty:
final reflection & gratitude

Darling, you've done it. Thirty days of self-discovery, shedding, re-working, planting, sowing, growing, and rooting into you, your why, and what's to come.

I believe all endings deserve to be honored. Like I said in week two of this workbook:

Everything in life a process of death and birth.
The hard part is letting death happen so that we can create new life.

I used to struggle with endings. The end of the day, the end of the school year, the end of relationships, the end of a show or a song or a date or long vacation. I was so fixated on riding the high. *What if I never feel this good again?* Letting something good end meant facing the mundane again.

181

Letting something good end meant living in the space between where everything is uncertain. All this did was lead to me chasing highs. Believing that my life was more designed by pain than pleasure, so if I experienced any ounce of joy, I'd better hold it tightly and milk it for all it was worth lest I never feel it in my arms again.

What I realized, though, is that the harder my grip on joy became, the looser my grip on pain. Pain became an untamable wave, and in the wake of my highest highs I experienced my lowest lows.

But all things end. This sentence has an ending. Each word has a final letter. That doesn't mean another word doesn't come after the period. That doesn't mean more books don't wait to be read. Resting my head on my pillow at night doesn't mean I won't wake in the morning.

I will die. So will you. Grief is in everything. So how do we cope? How do we allow ourselves to enjoy living, to enjoy the small nourishing moments, to enjoy each other's company while holding the truth that *everything will die?*

Gratitude. A reverence for what is. An appreciation for what's in front of us. An acknowledgment of the both/and: that this moment is good, and that it too will end.

I am grateful you chose to use this workbook. And I know that it's over. I am grateful to be alive. And I know it will end. I appreciate this moment where my fingers are typing in the sunlight, my best friend sitting across from me, hot coffee warming my insides. And I know this hour will pass.

Gratitude for what is. Acceptance for what was. Faith for what will be.

Today's Prompt: Reflect on the thirty days and *find gratitude.*

Look back at this entire experience. Think about how you felt before you started. Write about how you have grown, evolved, or learned during this process.

Here are some questions to help spark the reflection:

→ How has this challenge impacted you?

→ What has it sparked in you?

→ What has it inspired you to do next?

→ What are you grateful for from this process?

→ How can you honor that this practice is over, and hold faith that something good will come again?

WRITE *to* HEAL

date: _____

you may use the space below to write, or choose to write on your computer.

WEEK FOUR

WRITE *to* HEAL

congratulations, darling.
you *wrote to heal.*
I am so very proud of you.

WRITE *to* HEAL

acknowledgments

to anyone who has ever felt alone.

Special Thanks To:

Bella Begazo
Darla Wheatman, *Trauma Therapist*
Ilva Zonne
Jenna Edwards, MA, NCC
Jessica Kershaw
Kat Hall, *Planners By Kat*
Kim West, *Spoons & Sprouts Holistic Nutrition*
Kryza So Tiong
Lisa Mulder
Maritza Padilla
Samantha Breen
Sara Addalsee
Shelby Lavery, *Freelance Social Media Manager & Storyteller*

WRITE *to* HEAL

about the author

Rachel is the bestselling author of *Where the River Flows*, *The Inner Child Journal*, *The Self-Healer's Journal*, and *The Grief Workbook*. Using social media as a platform for her voice, she aims to destigmatize mental health and create safe spaces for people to be seen, understood, and feel less alone.

Rachel blends the wisdom and lessons from 18 years of therapy, eastern medicine, energy work, and study of psychology into a practice of paying it forward. With radical transparency, storytelling, and education, she encourages others to witness themselves as their own master of healing. Her current mantra: *show up messy, show up scared, show up uncertain, show up unprepared—whatever you do, just show up.*

Resilience, introspection, and honesty are at the heart of Rachel's work. She is truly grateful to connect with other healing and heart-centered souls through words, and thanks you for engaging in her work.

You can find her on Instagram at @rachel_havekost, twitter @rachelhavekost, TikTok @rachelhavekost, and on her website at www.rachelhavekost.com.

If you are interested in writing your own story, Rachel offers writing mentorships and would love to hear from you. You can make submissions through her website: www.rachelhavekost.com.

also by the author

The Self-Healer's Journal
The Inner Child Journal
The Grief Workbook
Where the River Flows: A Memoir of Love, Loss,
& Life With an Eating Disorder

Loved Write to Heal?

Tag me on social media!

Share your experience reading this book by tagging me on:
Instagram: @rachel_havekost
TikTok @rachelhavekost
Twitter: @rachel_havekost

Reviews are also a beautiful way to honor this work. Everything I write is in service of hopefully helping one person feel less alone. If that person is you, I would love your help in expanding this impact by sharing your experience. *If engaging with this work was meaningful to you in some way, your review might be the reason someone else finds themselves in its pages.*

Seeking Writing Consultation?

Book a call with Rachel and get support in the writing and publishing process. She welcomes inquiries and questions about consultations at rachel.havekost@gmail.com

WRITE *to* HEAL

Manufactured by Amazon.ca
Bolton, ON

38031826R00120